Compare Bears® Maths

Book 2

G000136271

Barbara Hewett

The Author

With twenty years experience of infant teaching, Barbara Hewitt
has lectured on teaching infant maths and ran a maths centre for
teachers. She now devotes her time to writing and tutoring, and has
many publications including contribution to a major primary maths
scheme.

Photocopying

Compare Bears may be ordered direct from LDA:
00943

Compare Bears Maths Book 2

00691
ISBN 1 85503 157 4

© Illustration Susan Perkins
© Text Barbara Hewett

COMPARE BEARS® is a registered trade mark.
Design of COMPARE BEARS © Learning Resources, Inc.

LDA, Duke Street, Wisbech, Cambs PE13 2AE, England

Introduction

Compare Bears Maths Book 2 is designed for use with the Compare Bears and is compatible with any infant mathematics scheme for children at Year 1 and 2.

Compare Bears Maths Book 2 has a full range of mathematical activities covering:

- vertical and horizontal addition and subtraction
- division and multiplication in equal sets
- odd and even numbers
- games for place value
- sorting grids and trees
- halves and quarters
- investigations and problems
- time and money
- left and right orientation
- probability

The majority of worksheets cover numbers up to 20, giving children plenty of practice through the difficult 'teens' area.

Photocopying material usually leaves the reverse side of the paper unused. To help cut down on this waste, each Compare Bears worksheet has further ideas for activities which can be written on the back of the sheet. These extension activities are flashed by a symbol of the back of a bear.

Sometimes space does not allow the Compare Bears to be placed on the worksheet itself, as for instance on Sheet 4, 'Make up 4 sums…'. Here, the bears should be placed on the table in front of the child.

Always have Compare Bears available for work with all the worksheets.

On completion of each worksheet, children should be asked to talk about what they have done, how they did it and describe any number patterns they have discovered.

The topics can be used in any order. They will reinforce areas in the schools mathematics scheme, particularly for children who need further practice in basic number work.

The problems and investigations work will be a challenge to children (and teachers). They should be encouraged to work to an orderly pattern when they are looking for numbers. For example, the fare for the bears in boats should begin with 1p and 1p and 1p. By changing one fare at a time – 1p and 1p and 2p, they gradually arrive at 3p and 3p and 3p. In this way a pattern emerges which ensures that all the alternatives are covered and any omission can be 'seen'.

As there are several types of this investigation, it would be worthwhile to work through one of these activities on the blackboard with the whole class. This would demonstrate how to make an order and pattern in an investigation.

Compare Bears can be a useful and fun way of involving parents in maths work. When the games are mounted, coloured and covered, they can be allowed home with a die and appropriate bears. The investigations are often new to parents and they too find them an interesting challenge.

Prepare a Compare Bears corner in the classroom where you can display the children's work and the bears. Put out:

- bears to be counted, matched and sorted,
- sets to be made and shared,
- patterns and sequences to be continued,
- games to be played,
- bears and money to be bought and sold,
- scales for bears to be weighed.

Children can build homes for the Compare Bears with their construction kits and scrap materials to practise their counting and measuring skills. They should be encouraged to use their imagination and make up stories (number stories of course) about the Compare Bears, giving them individual names and adventures.

Mathematics in this way will have a real meaning for children. Encourage them to carry out their own activities with the Compare Bears, talk about their ideas, work together and enjoy 'doing maths'.

A photocopy master for Compare Bears cut-outs in three sizes is on page 84. These can be cut up, and made available for the children to colour and use with the activity sheets.

A photocopy master of templates for dice can be found on page 81. These can be mounted on thin card and constructed for use with the games throughout.

A photocopy master of 100 square is on page 83. This should be mounted on card, covered and made available to the children at all times. It can be used with the smallest Compare Bears and helps children to 'see' the pattern of numbers, with sequencing, counting on and back, multiplying and dividing and place value.

Some children may need help in reading the instructions and drawing the grids. They may also require help in drawing bears where requested. These children may find it preferable to use the bear templates from page 84.

In this second edition we have made one change.

The words 'daddy', 'mummy' and 'baby' have been replaced with the words 'large', 'medium' and 'small'.

The work in this book complements the following schemes:

1 HEINEMANN
   Mathematics – 3

2 GINN
   Mathematics – Level 2

3 LONGMAN
   Primary Maths Levels 2 and 3

4 CAMBRIDGE UNIVERSITY PRESS
   Cambridge Primary Mathematics – Modules 2 and 3

5 NELSON
   Nelson Mathematics Towards Level 2
   Maths Chest 3

6 COLLINS
   Steps – Level 2

A complete range of Compare Bears® materials are available from LDA:

00943	Compare Bears
00613	Compare Bears Maths Book 1
00633	Balancing Bears
00638	Attribute Cards
00695	Compare Bears Stamps
00885	Compare Bears Bingo
00735	Compare Bears Stickers
00745	Compare Bears Science and Technology

The bears are also available in a number of different colour and size combinations.

Contents

Activity Sheet	Title	Activity	Programme of Study (KS1)	Activity Sheet	Title	Activity	Programme of Study (KS1)
38	Systematic recording	*arranging bears around the dinner table*	Number 5b	53	A handful of bears	*sorting with 2 attributes*	Number 5b
39	Systematic recording	*drawing bears in different rooms*	Number 5b	54	Money to 10p	*buying bears using 1p, 2p, and 5p*	Number 4a
40	Addition: numbers up to 20	*adding bears and completing the sums*	Number 3c	55	Money to 20p	*buying bears*	Number 4a
41	Vertical addition: numbers up to 20	*adding bears and completing the sums*	Number 3c	56	Multiplication	*writing the tables of 2 and 3*	Number 4b
42	Vertical addition: numbers up to 20	*adding bears and completing the sums*	Number 3c	57	Multiplication	*writing the tables for 5 and 10*	Number 4b
43	Addition and subtraction: numbers up to 20	*adding and subtracting bears to complete the sums*	Number 3c	58	Multiplication	*dividing bears into equal sets*	Number 4b
44	Addition	*counting in 10s*	Number 3b	59	Multiplication	*dividing bears into equal sets*	Number 4b
45	A sorting grid	*sorting with 2 attributes*	Number 5a	60	Money	*finding change from a 10p coin*	Number 4a
46	Division	*dividing 12 into equal groups*	Number 3c	61	Money	*finding change from a 20p coin*	Number 4a
47	Addition: numbers up to 20	*counting in 2s, 3s, and 4s*	Number 3b	62	Money	*exchanging 1p coins for 2p coins*	Number 4a
48	Division	*dividing bears into equal groups*	Number 4b	63	Place value	*Exchange game 3*	Number 2b
49	Multiplication	*writing the table of 2*	Number 3c	64	Left and right orientation	*finding different combinations of left and right facing pairs*	Shape 3a
50	Division	*dividing the bears into equal sets of 2*	Number 3c	65	Addition	*adding 3 numbers to make 11 and 12*	Number 3c
51	Number patterns	*adding and recording rows of bears*	Number 3c	66	Subtraction	*subtracting 3 numbers from 11 and 12*	Number 3c
52	Multiplication	*writing the table of 2*	Number 3c	67	Systematic recording	*making different tunes*	Number 5b
				68	Systematic recording	*leading the bear to the honey*	Number 5b
				69	Halves and quarters	*putting bears into squares*	Number 2a

Activity Sheet	Title	Activity	Programme of Study (KS1)
70	Halves and quarters	*dividing 4 and 6 equally*	Number 2b
71	Halves and quarters	*dividing 8 equally*	Number 2b
72	Probability – a frequency table	*collecting and recording data*	Number 5b
73	Probability – a frequency table	*collecting and recording data*	Number 5b
74	Number patterns: numbers up to 20	*subtracting from 20*	Number 3c
75	Number patterns: numbers up to 20	*adding with 10s*	Number 3c
76	Addition	*adding 3 numbers to make 20*	Number 3c
77	Addition	*exploring the bonds of 10*	Number 3c
78	A sorting grid	*sorting by 2 attributes*	Number 5a
79	Multiplication	*counting in 4s and 8s*	Number 3c
80	Multiplication	*counting in 8s and 10s*	Number 3c

COMPARE BEARS WORK

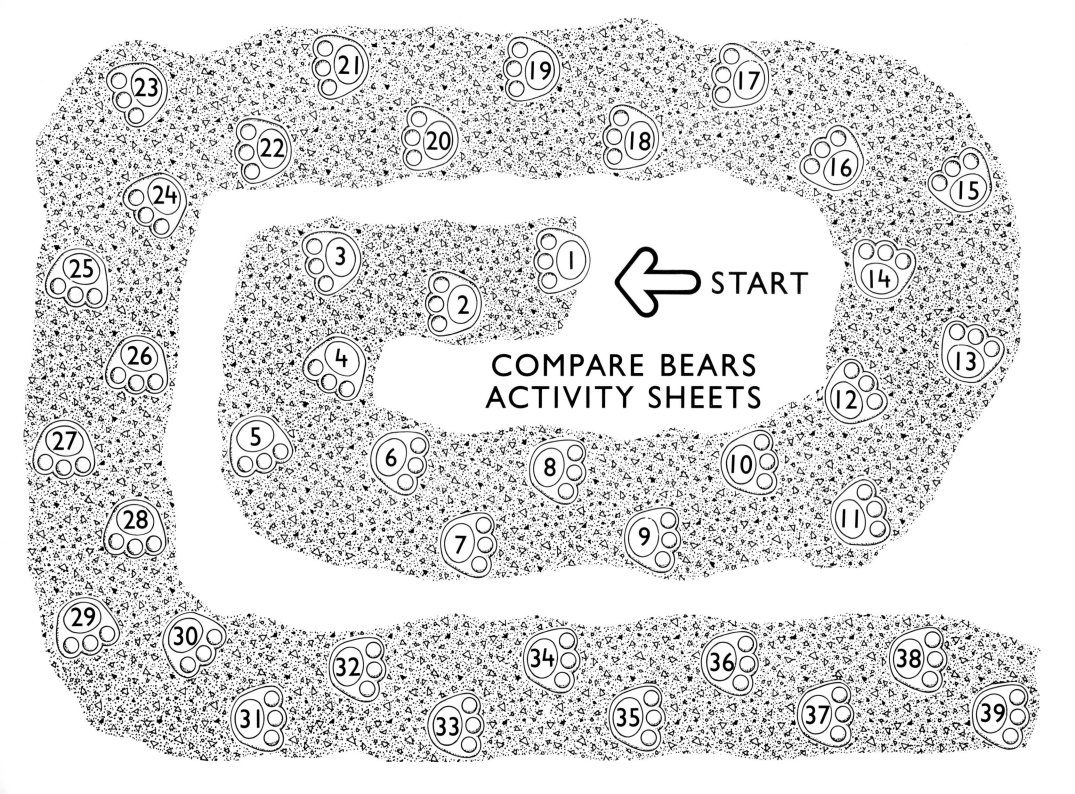

START

COMPARE BEARS
ACTIVITY SHEETS

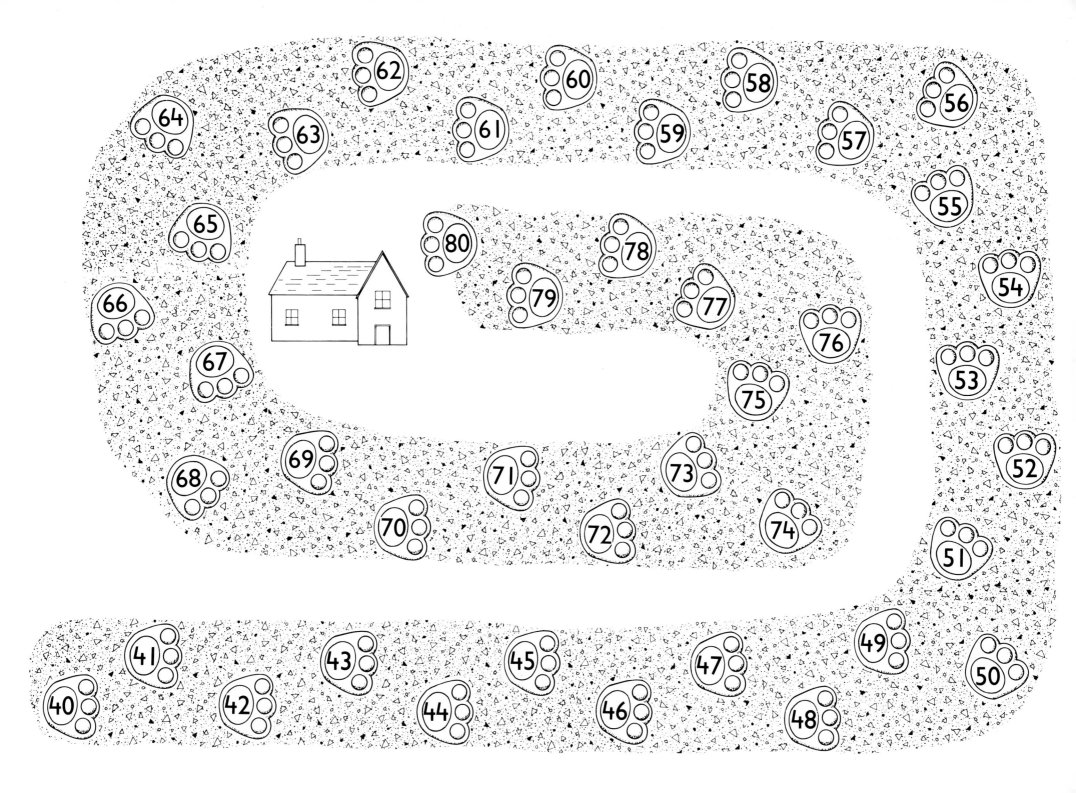

Put a bear in each square and fill in the numbers.

1	2							

1	2	3

Number the squares.
Put the bears in rows of 3.

How many groups of 3? ☐
How many bears altogether? ☐

Put a ring round all the odd numbers.

Write the numbers 1–10. Ring the even numbers. ⇨

Take 6 bears.

Make up 4 sums. $2 + 4 = 6$ $6 - 4 = \boxed{}$ $4 + 2 = \boxed{}$ $6 - 2 = \boxed{}$

Take 7 bears.

Make up 4 sums. $2 + 5 = \boxed{}$ _____

Take 8 bears.

Make up 4 sums. $2 + 6 = \boxed{}$ _____

Take 9 bears.

Make up 4 sums. $2 + 7 = \boxed{}$ _____

Take 10 bears.

Make up 4 sums. $2 + 8 = \boxed{}$ _____

Make up 4 different sums for 6 and 7 bears.   ⇨

Take 7 bears.

Complete the sums.

$3 + 4 = \square$
$4 + 3 = \square$
$7 - 4 = \square$
$7 - 3 = \square$

$7 = 3 + \square$
$7 = \square + 3$
$7 - \square = 4$
$7 - \square = 3$

$\square + 3 = 7$
$\square + 4 = 7$
$\square - 3 = 4$
$\square - 4 = 3$

$6 + 1 = \square$
$1 + 6 = \square$
$7 - 1 = \square$

$7 = 6 + \square$
$7 = \square + 1$
$7 - 6 = \square$

$\square - 6 = 1$
$\square + 1 = 7$
$\square - 1 = 6$

Make up sums for 8 and 9 ⇨

Using the bears, make up 4 sums. Use the same numbers.

1 + 2 = ☐	1 + 3 = 4	1 + 5 = 6
2 + 1 = ☐	_____	_____
3 − 1 = ☐	_____	_____
3 − 2 = ☐	_____	_____
2 + 3 = 5	1 + 7 = 8	1 + 8 = 9
_____	_____	_____
_____	_____	_____
_____	_____	_____

Make up 4 sums with these numbers 1,4,5   1,6,7   2,3,5 ⇨

Number the stools. Put bears on the stools. Count and complete the sums.

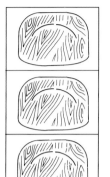

$$6 + 2$$

$$4 + 5$$

$$4 + 3$$

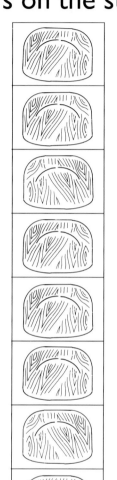

$$3 + 5$$

$$1 + 4$$

$$9 + 0$$

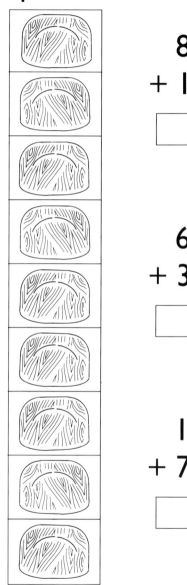

$$8 + 1$$

$$6 + 3$$

$$1 + 7$$

Draw a house for the bears. Put in 1 , 2 🌳, 3 🐦, 4 ⊞ . Choose your own pictures for 5, 6, 7, 8, 9 and 10. ⇨

© LDA Compare Bears Maths Book 2

Number the stools. Put bears on the stools. Count and complete the sums.

3
2
1

$$5 - 3 = \boxed{}$$

$$6 - 0 = \boxed{}$$

$$7 - 4 = \boxed{}$$

$$6 - 3 = \boxed{}$$

$$9 - 6 = \boxed{}$$

$$8 - 5 = \boxed{}$$

$$9 - 7 = \boxed{}$$

$$8 - 2 = \boxed{}$$

$$7 - 2 = \boxed{}$$

10 bears went to a party. 1 bear went home.
How many bears were left? $10 - 1 = \boxed{}$. Write the sums as each bear leaves the party. ➪

Place bears in the spaces. Find the difference between the rows.

The difference between 5 and 2 is ☐

The difference between ☐ and ☐ is ☐

The difference between ☐ and ☐ is ☐

Make up some more rows of bears and find the difference between them. ⇨

Number the spaces. Put out bears to match the spaces.

1	2	3	4	5			
1	2	3	4	5	6	7	8

Complete the sentences.

5 is ☐ less than 8

8 is ☐ more than 4

6 is ☐ fewer than 8

Take 6 bears. Find the difference between 6 and 0, 6 and 1, 6 and 2, 6 and 3, and so on.

Number the spaces. Put out bears to match the spaces.

1	2	3

1								

Complete the number sentences.

3 and ☐ make 9

4 more than ☐ is 9

☐ and 2 make 9

Take 7 bears. Find the difference between 7 and 0, 7 and 1, 7 and 2 and so on. ⇨

© LDA Compare Bears Maths Book 2

Sit the bears on the stools. Count them. Draw or stick 1 fewer in each ring.

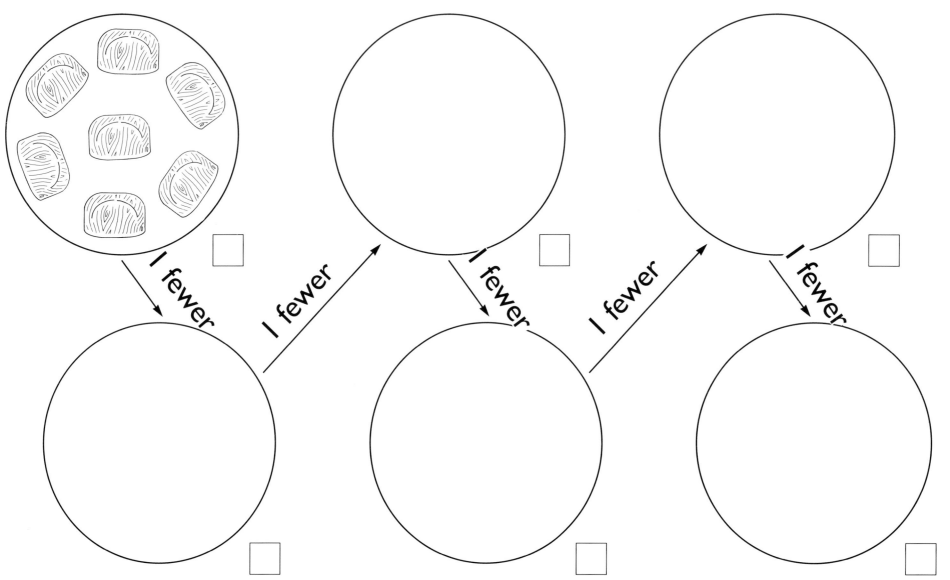

Start with 10 bears. Draw or stick 2 fewer each time. ⇨

Use bears. Count in twos.

$+ 2$ →

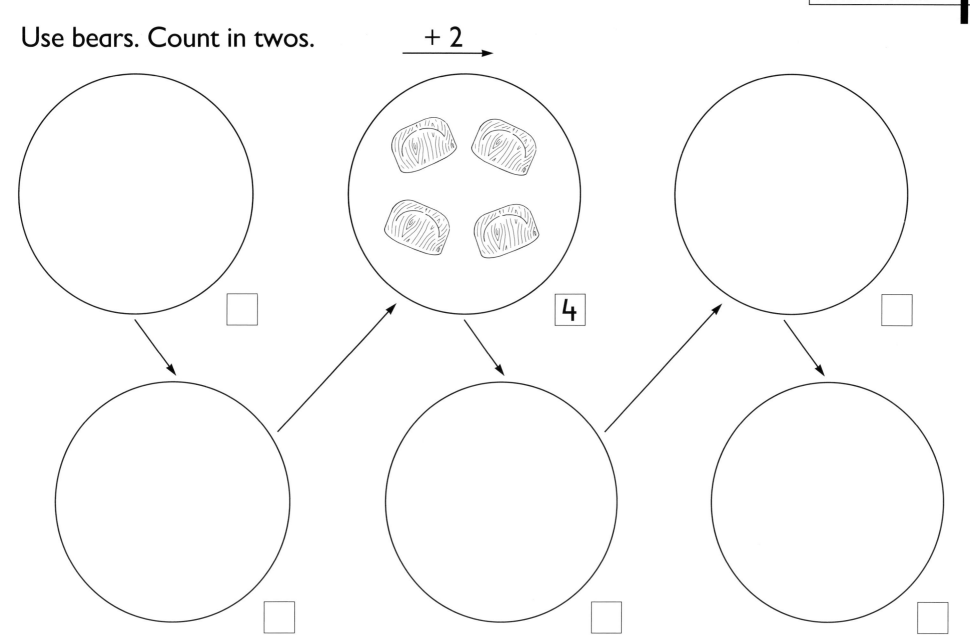

Start with 1 bear and add 2 each time. ⇨

Colour the stools. Match the bears to the stools. Write the story of 5.

      $5 = 5 + 0$

      $5 = 4 + \square$

      $5 = \square + \square$

      $5 = \square + \square$

      $5 = \square + \square$

Write the stories for 6, 7, 8, 9 and 10 ⇨

Place bears in the spaces. Number the spaces.

	1	2	3								

Divide the bears into 2 equal sets.

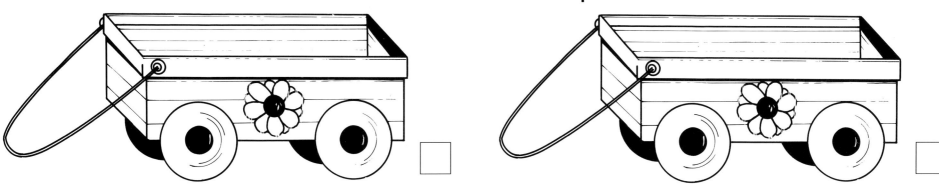

Divide each group into 2 equal sets.

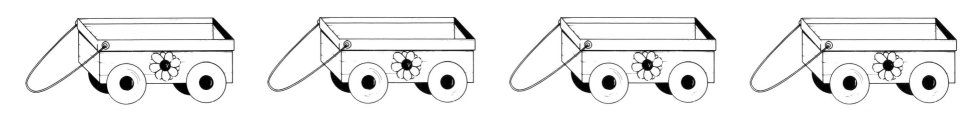

How many bears in each set? ☐ How many sets? ☐

Divide 4, 6, 8 and 10 bears into 2 equal sets. Draw or stick them in the sets. ⇨

A game for 2 players. You need 2 dice, 9 green bears and 9 yellow bears.

green board

5	8	6
3	2	9
12	4	7

yellow board

10	2	4
6	3	8
7	11	5

Throw the dice. Add together the scores. Cover the number with a bear.
The first completed board is the winner.

Colour the stools. Match the bears to the stools. Draw lines to divide the colours. How many subsets? ☐

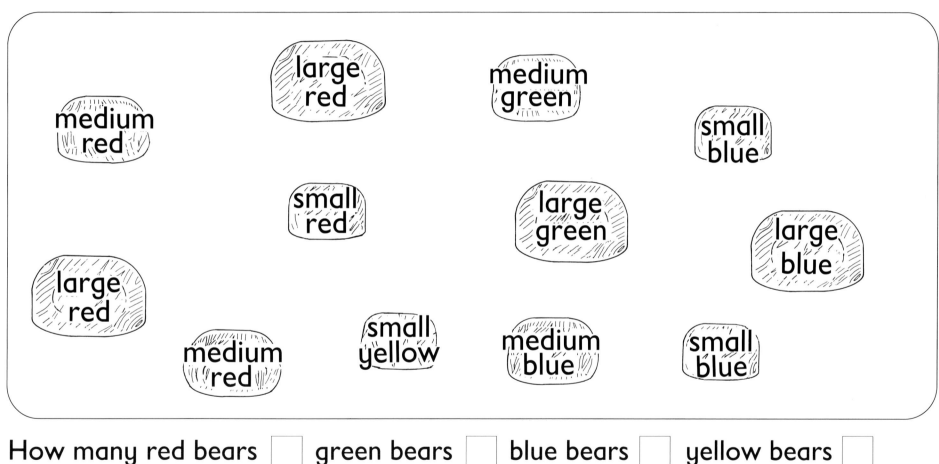

How many red bears ☐ green bears ☐ blue bears ☐ yellow bears ☐

How many bears altogether? ☐

Draw or stick a set of 13 bears. Use 4 colours. Count the subsets. ⇨

10 bears played hide and seek in the garden. They hid behind 2 bushes.
Draw the hiding bears.

5

then behind 3 bushes

then behind 4 bushes

then behind 5 bushes

Play the game again, this time with 9 bears.

Write the numbers in order.

Write the numbers 0 to 15 in order forwards and backwards. ⇨

Fill in the missing numbers.

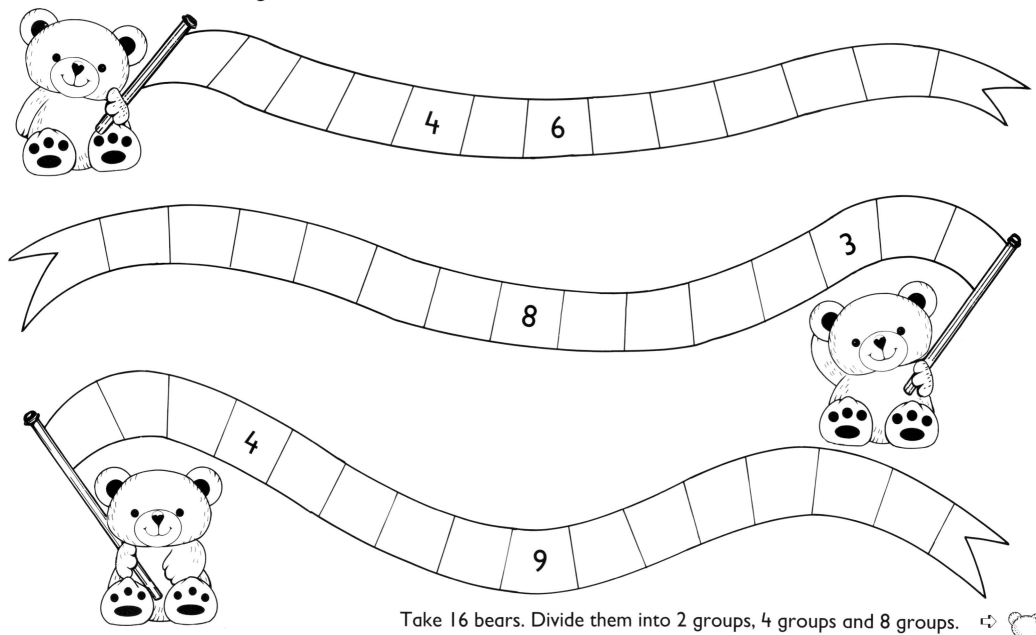

Take 16 bears. Divide them into 2 groups, 4 groups and 8 groups. ⇨

Divide the numbers 1 to 10 into two groups.

odd numbers

| 1 | | | |

even numbers

| 2 | | | |

Use bears. Add together
2 numbers from the odd group. ☐ + ☐ = ☐

Is the answer an odd or even number? _____

2 numbers from the even group ☐ + ☐ = ☐ _____

1 number from each group ☐ + ☐ = ☐ _____

Try some more numbers ☐ + ☐ = ☐ _____

☐ + ☐ = ☐ _____

Add together the other numbers. Say if the answers are odd or even numbers. ⇨

A game for 2 players. You need one bear die, 1 board, 20 small and 4 large bears. Throw the die and put the right number of small bears on the curve. You must throw the exact number to finish the curve. When you have 10 small bears, you can exchange them for a large bear. The first player to collect 2 large bears is the winner.

Sit medium bears on the stools. Give them 2 small bears each.

Write the table.

1	medium bear has	2	small bears
2	medium bears have	☐	small bears
3		☐	
4		☐	
5		☐	
6		☐	
7		☐	
8		☐	

Give the medium bears 3 small bears each. Write the table.

1	medium bear has	3	small bears
2	medium bears have	☐	small bears
3		☐	
4		☐	
5		☐	
6		☐	
7		☐	
8		☐	

Use only red and blue medium and large bears on this sorting tree.

Name all the regions – 'red' – 'not red'.

Take one bear at a time. Find where they belong.

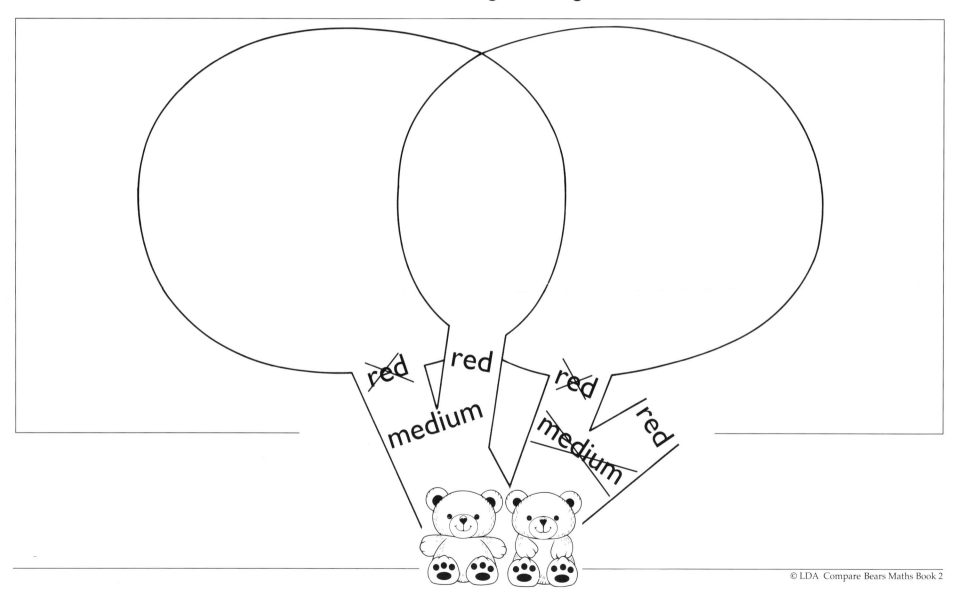

Use the red and blue bears. Sort the bears and count them.

	large	medium	small
red			
blue			

red bears ☐ blue bears ☐ large bears ☐ medium bears ☐

Sort and count the green and yellow bears in the same way. ⇨

Use the red bears only.

Put bears in the squares so that no two that are the same size are next to each other.
Draw or stick the sizes.

Use the blue and yellow bears.

Put bears in the squares so that no two that are the same size or colour are next to each other.
Draw and colour the sizes.

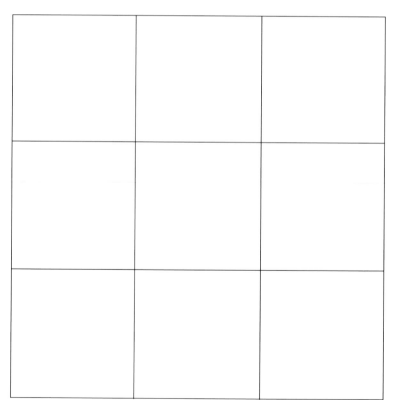

Take the bears through the house. Change the size.

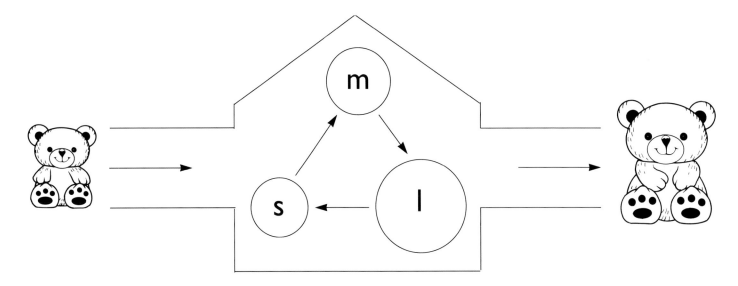

Write the changes.

small red bear   ⟶   medium red bear

large green bear   ⟶   _____

medium yellow bear   ⟶   _____

small blue bear   ⟶   _____

large red bear   ⟶   _____

small green bear   ⟶   _____

Take the bears through the house. Change the size and colour.

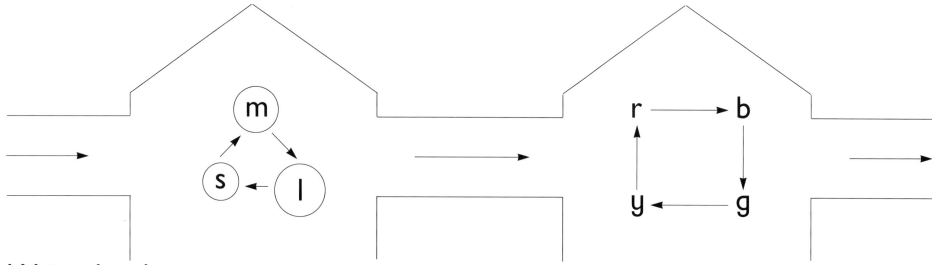

Write the changes.

small red bear ———————→ medium red bear ———————→ medium blue bear _____

large green bear ———————→ _____ ———————→ _____

medium yellow bear ———————→ _____ ———————→ _____

small blue bear ———————→ _____ ———————→ _____

large red bear ———————→ _____ ———————→ _____

small green bear ———————→ _____ ———————→ _____

Draw 2 more changing houses with different changes. Take some more bears through. ⇨

The bears like buns.

Cut 1 bun in half 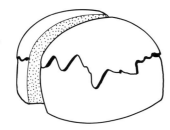 and then into quarters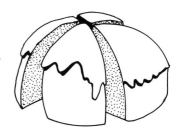

How many bears can have a quarter each? ☐

Complete the table.

buns	halves	quarters	how many bears have a quarter
1	2		
2			
3			
4			
5			

Draw 6 bears and 3 buns – how many quarters can each bear have? ⇨

Take 8 small yellow bears and 10 small blue bears. Line them up in 2 rows.

Row 1.   1 blue   3 yellow   1 blue   3 yellow   1 blue.

Row 2.   2 blue   1 yellow   3 blue   1 yellow   2 blue.

Colour this pattern on to the squares. Repeat the two rows again.

Find some squared paper and make up some more patterns of your own. Choose two colours with the bears.

Choose 4 bears. Each one must be a different colour.

Arrange them in the spaces.

How many different ways can you arrange the bears?

Colour the small squares.

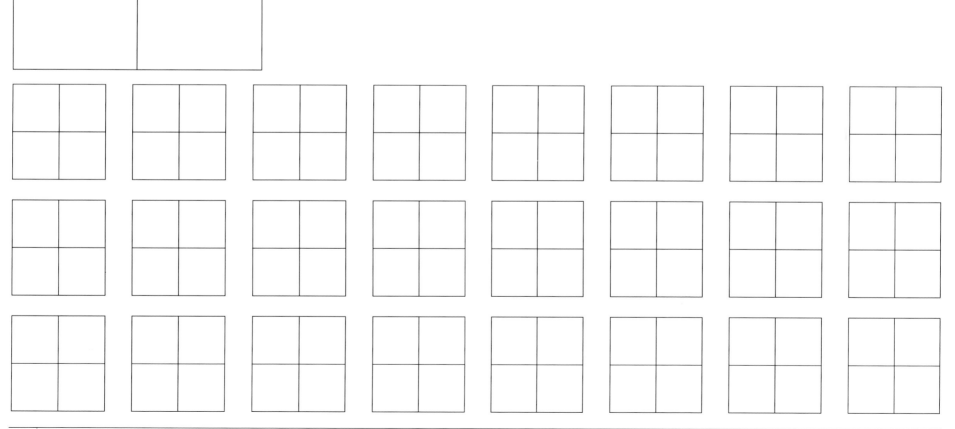

Take I green, I red, I blue medium bear. I green, I red, I blue large bear.

How many different pairs of medium and large bears can you make? Colour the spaces.

Add I medium and I large bear of another colour. How many more different pairs can you make? ⇨

Take 3 bears. Find different ways for them to sail in the boats. They can sail alone or in twos or threes.

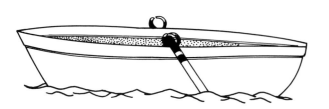

| Fare 1p | | | | Fare 2p | | | Fare 3p |

Bear 1	Bear 2	Bear 3	Cost	Bear 1	Bear 2	Bear 3	Cost
1p	1p	1p	3p				

Find some different ways for 4 bears to sail in the boats. Work out the cost. ⇨

The red bear found himself at a maze.

How many different routes could he take to find his way to the honey?

He used a path only once. Draw his routes on the squares.

A game for 2 players.
You will need 1 board each. 1 die.
Throw a die and put small bears on the 10 grid.
When there are more than 10 small bears, put the extra bears in the holding place.
Exchange the 10 small bears for 1 large bear.
Put the bears in the holding place on the grid and start again.
The winner is the first player with 5 large bears.

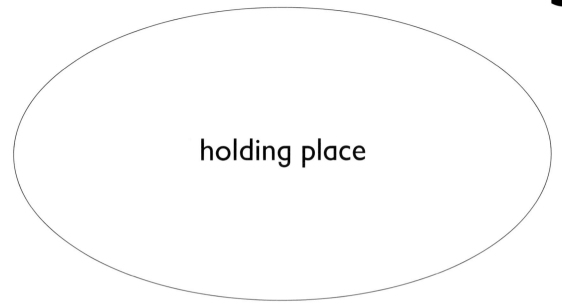

holding place

1	2	3	4	5
6	7	8	9	10

large bears				

A game for 2 players. I die. I player has all the small red bears. The other player has all the small green bears. Throw the die. Place a bear on a time to match the score. The winner is the first player with three bears in a row, a column or a diagonal.

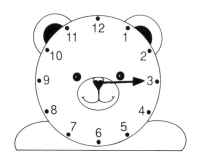

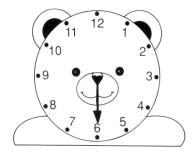

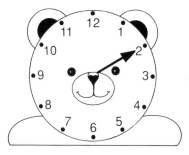

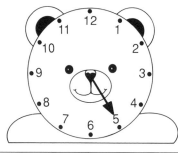

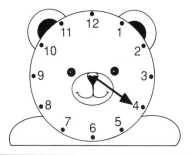

A game for 2 players. 2 dice. I player has all the medium red bears. The other player has all the medium blue bears. Throw the dice and place a bear on a time to match the score. The winner is the first player to have three bears in a row, column or diagonal.

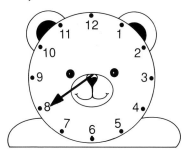  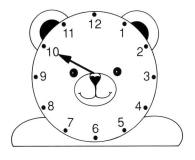 

 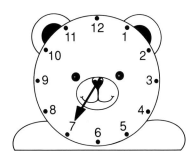  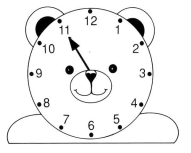

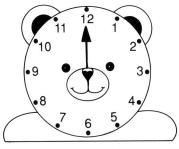   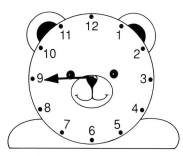

The green bear and the red bear have 4 party hats.

Show the different ways they can wear the hats.

Show the different ways 3 bears can wear the hats.

Use the bears to help fill in the addition square. Choose a number from the bottom row and add a number from the side column.

Write the answer in the square.

+	6	7	8	9	10
10					
9					
8		15			
7				16	
6					

On the back, copy the square and subtract the smaller number from the greater number. ⇨

The bears sit on different stools round the table.

Colour 1 stool in a different place round the table.

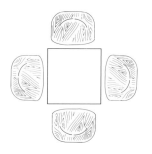 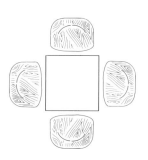 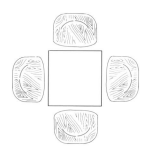 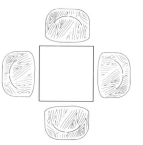

Colour 2 stools in a different place round the table.

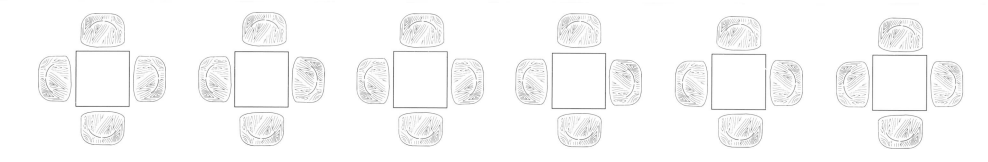

Colour 3 stools in different places round the table.

Draw 1 bear in a different room in each house.

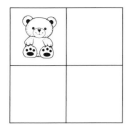 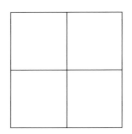 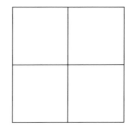 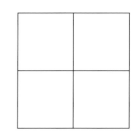

Draw 2 bears in different rooms in each house.

 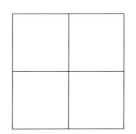 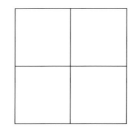 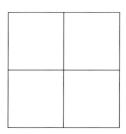

Draw 3 bears in different rooms in each house.

 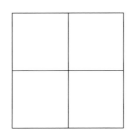 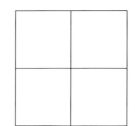

Use small bears. Line them up in the spaces.

1	2	3	4	5	6	7	8	9	10	11	12	13	14	15	16	17	18

Complete the sums.

6 + 8 = ☐	7 + 7 = ☐
9 + 8 = ☐	3 + 9 = ☐
5 + 7 = ☐	8 + 5 = ☐
4 + 9 = ☐	6 + 6 = ☐
8 + 8 = ☐	6 + 9 = ☐
7 + 6 = ☐	7 + 9 = ☐
3 + 8 = ☐	8 + 7 = ☐

Write the number bonds of 11 and 12. ⇨

Use small bears. Fill the spaces. Complete the sums.

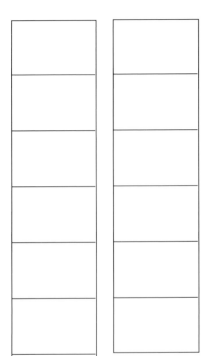

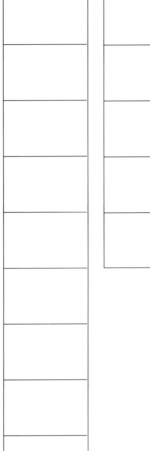

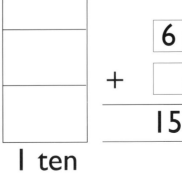

```
    9                8                6                4
  +               +                +                +
 ─────            ─────            ─────            ─────
   16               12               15               13
```

1 ten   1 ten   1 ten   1 ten

Use small bears. Fill the ten column. Complete the sums.

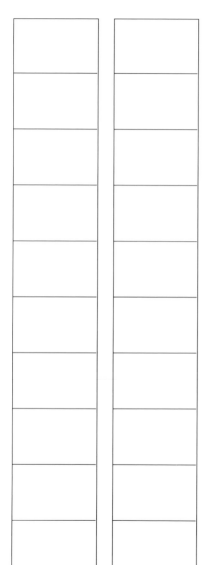

ten

```
    9          8          6
+   9      +   7      +   5
_____    _____    _____


    8          6          7
+   3      +   9      +   7
_____    _____    _____


    5          6          9
+   8      +   7      +   5
_____    _____    _____
```

Write the number bonds for 15 and 16. ⇨

Use 10 yellow and 10 green small bears.

10 + 1 = ☐   20 − 10 = ☐

10 + ☐ = 12   19 − 10 = ☐

10 + 3 = ☐   18 − 10 = ☐

10 + 4 = ☐   11 − 10 = ☐

☐ + 5 = 15   16 − 10 = ☐

10 + ☐ = 16   12 − 10 = ☐

10 + 7 = ☐   14 − 10 = ☐

☐ + 8 = 18   17 − 10 = ☐

10 + 9 = ☐   15 − 10 = ☐

10 + 10 = ☐   13 − 10 = ☐

Write the number bonds for 17 and 18. ⇨

You need all the bears.

Collect and count.

1 All the medium bears.   How many tens? ☐

2 All the small blue and green bears.   ⟶ ☐

3 All the medium and large bears.   ⟶ ☐

4 All the large bears and all the small red bears.   ⟶ ☐

5 All the small blue and red bears and all
   the medium blue and red bears.   ⟶ ☐

6 All the large, medium and small green bears.   ⟶ ☐

7 All the small bears and all the medium bears.   ⟶ ☐

8 All the green and yellow bears.   ⟶ ☐

Count in tens. Start at 0, 1 and 2. ⇨

Sort and count all the bears. Fill in the table.

	red	blue	green	yellow
large bear				
medium bear				
small bear				

How many: small bears?

large, medium and small red bears?

medium red, blue and green bears?

large blue, green and yellow bears and small blue bears?

medium yellow bears and small red, blue and green bears?

all the large, medium and small bears?

Count in fives. Start at 0, 1 and 2. ⇨

Take 12 bears. Put them in equal sets. Count the bears in each set.

Make 2 sets.   How many in each set?   [ ]

3   ——————————————————→   [ ]

4   ——————————————————→   [ ]

6   ——————————————————→   [ ]

Complete the table.

number of sets	number in each set	number altogether
2		12
4		

Take 16 bears. Put them in 2, 4 and 8 equal sets. Make a table.

Take 20 bears.

Count in twos.

2   4   6

Count in fours.

4   8

Count in threes.

3   6

Count in twos.   Start with 1 bear.

1   3   5

Count in fours.   Start with 1 bear.

1   5

Take 30 bears. Count in threes, fours and fives. Start with 2 bears. ⇨

Take 20 bears. Divide them into equal sets. Write the number of sets. Finish the table. Check that you start with the right number of bears.

Number of bears	Number in each set	Number of sets
20	2	
20		5
21	3	
24	4	
24		8
25	5	
27	3	
28	4	
30	5	

Take 20 bears. Count back in twos, fours and fives. Start at 20. ⇨

Use small red and blue bears.
Complete the table of 2.

Number of sets	Number in each set	Number of bears
1	2	2
2	2	

Draw or stick bears in sets of 3. Write the table of 3. ⇨

• •

Divide the bears into sets of 2.
Use small bears.

Number of bears	Number in each set	Number of sets
4	2	2
12	2	
8	2	
2	2	
18	2	
14	2	
6	2	
20	2	
16	2	
10	2	

Count back in threes. Start at 30. ⇨

Put the bears in rows. Start with 1 bear. Count the bears. Keep the record.

1			
1	2		
1	2	3	

Row	Number of bears altogether
1	1
2	3
3	

Make 10 rows.

Look for a pattern in the numbers.

Find the difference between the numbers in the columns.

Count back in fours. Start at 40.

Each medium bear has 2 small bears.

Complete the table for the number of bears altogether.

Look for a pattern in the columns of numbers.

medium bears	small bears	bears altogether
1	2	3
2	4	
3		

Write a table for 1 medium and 3 small bears. Find the number of bears altogether. ⇨

Take 3 handfuls of bears. Record them on the chart.

KEY

r	=	red	l	=	large
bl	=	blue	m	=	medium
g	=	green	s	=	small
y	=	yellow			

Colour 1 space for each bear.

	r : l	r : m	r : s	bl : l	bl : m	bl : s	g : l	g : m	g : s	y : l	y : m	y : s
6												
5												
4												
3												
2												
1												

There are ⬚ red bears ⬚ blue bears ⬚ green bears ⬚ yellow bears.

There are ⬚ bears altogether.

Find some more things to say about this chart. ⇨

Colour the coins you could use to buy the bears.

a large bear 10p

a medium bear 8p

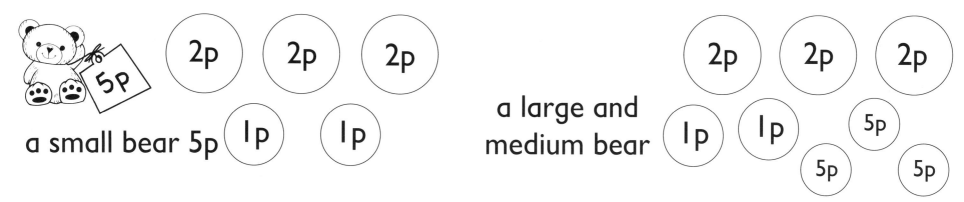

a small bear 5p

a large and medium bear

Draw the coins you use to buy 2 large bears, 2 medium bears and 2 small bears. ⇨

a large bear 10p

a medium bear 8p

a small bear 5p

buy 2 large bears ☐ p

+ ☐ p

―――

☐ p

2 medium bears ☐ p

+ ☐ p

―――

☐ p

2 small bears ☐ p

+ ☐ p

―――

☐ p

1 medium bear ☐ p

1 large bear + ☐ p

―――

☐ p

1 large bear ☐ p

1 small bear + ☐ p

―――

☐ p

1 medium bear ☐ p

1 small bear + ☐ p

―――

☐ p

How much will it cost to buy all the large and small red bears? ⇨

Complete the tables.

1 small bear costs [2] p

2 small bears cost [ ] p

3 ⟶ [ ] p

4 ⟶ [ ] p

5 ⟶ [ ] p

6 ⟶ [ ] p

7 ⟶ [ ] p

8 ⟶ [ ] p

9 ⟶ [ ] p

10 ⟶ [ ] p

1 medium bear costs [3] p

2 medium bears cost [ ] p

3 ⟶ [ ] p

4 ⟶ [ ] p

5 ⟶ [ ] p

6 ⟶ [ ] p

7 ⟶ [ ] p

8 ⟶ [ ] p

9 ⟶ [ ] p

10 ⟶ [ ] p

Complete the tables.

1 medium bear costs	5	p
2 medium bears cost		p
3 ⟶		p
4 ⟶		p
5 ⟶		p
6 ⟶		p
7 ⟶		p
8 ⟶		p
9 ⟶		p
10 ⟶		p

1 large bear costs	10	p
2 large bears cost		p
3 ⟶		p
4 ⟶		p
5 ⟶		p
6 ⟶		p
7 ⟶		p
8 ⟶		p
9 ⟶		p
10 ⟶		p

How many bears altogether?

2 threes are ☐

3 twos are ☐

2 fives are ☐

5 twos are ☐

2 fours are ☐

4 twos are ☐

How many bears for 2 fives, 2 sixes, 2 sevens. 2 eights, 2 nines and 2 tens? ⇨

Divide bears into equal sets. Draw the sets.

4 is ☐ twos

9 is ☐ threes

16 is ☐ fours

25 is ☐ fives

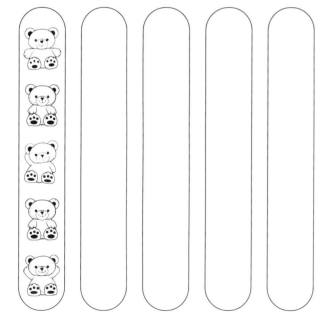

How many bears do you need for 3 sets of 4, 3 sets of 5, 3 sets of 6, 4 sets of 2, 4 sets of 3, 4 sets of 5? Draw the sets. ⇨

Buy the bears. Find the change from 10p.

Use 10p

Buy 1 large bear   change from 10p is ☐ p

1 medium bear ————————————————→ ☐ p

1 small bear ————————————————→ ☐ p

2 medium bears ———————————————→ ☐ p

2 small bears ————————————————→ ☐ p

3 small bears ————————————————→ ☐ p

1 medium and 1 small bear ————————————→ ☐ p

Use 15p. Buy the bears again. Find your change. ⇨

Buy the bears. Find the change from 20p.

Use 20p

Buy	1 large bear	change from 20p is	☐ p
	1 medium bear	⟶	☐ p
	1 small bear	⟶	☐ p
	2 large bears	⟶	☐ p
	3 medium bears	⟶	☐ p
	3 small bears	⟶	☐ p
	4 small bears	⟶	☐ p

Find other ways to buy the bears with 20p. ⇨

The small blue bear collects penny coins. Each time he has two, the medium bear changes them for a two pence coin.

How many 2p coins does the small bear have? Fill in the table.

Number of penny coins	Number of two penny coins	One penny coins left over	small blue bear has
2	1	0	2p
3	1	1	
4			
5			
6			
7			
8			
9			
10			

Show different ways to make 20p. Use 1p, 2p, 5p and 10p coins. ⇨

Bear's exchange. A game for 2 players.

Each player needs 1 board and 1 family of bears. 1 die.

1 family consists of: 5 large, 5 medium and 10 small bears.

The players throw the die in turn, pick up small bears only and place them in the spaces.

2 small bears can be exchanged for 1 medium bear. 2 medium bears can be exchanged for 1 large bear.

The winner is the first player to complete a board.

small bear	small bear							

medium bear			

large bear			

I bear can face only 2 ways.

to the right or to the left

Find 4 different ways for 2 bears.

Here are 2 ways.

Find 2 other ways.

Find different ways for 3 bears.

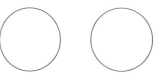 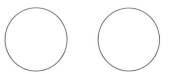

How many different ways can 4 bears face?

Divide 11 bears into 3 groups.

11 = [1] + [1] + [9]

11 = [ ] + [ ] + [ ]

11 = [ ] + [ ] + [ ]

11 = [ ] + [ ] + [ ]

11 = [ ] + [ ] + [ ]

11 = [ ] + [ ] + [ ]

11 = [ ] + [ ] + [ ]

11 = [ ] + [ ] + [ ]

11 = [ ] + [ ] + [ ]

11 = [ ] + [ ] + [ ]

Divide 12 bears into 3 groups.

12 = [1] + [2] + [9]

12 = [ ] + [ ] + [ ]

12 = [ ] + [ ] + [ ]

12 = [ ] + [ ] + [ ]

12 = [ ] + [ ] + [ ]

12 = [ ] + [ ] + [ ]

12 = [ ] + [ ] + [ ]

12 = [ ] + [ ] + [ ]

12 = [ ] + [ ] + [ ]

12 = [ ] + [ ] + [ ]

Divide 13 and 14 into 3 groups. ⇨

Subtract 3 numbers from 11.

Subtract 3 numbers from 12.

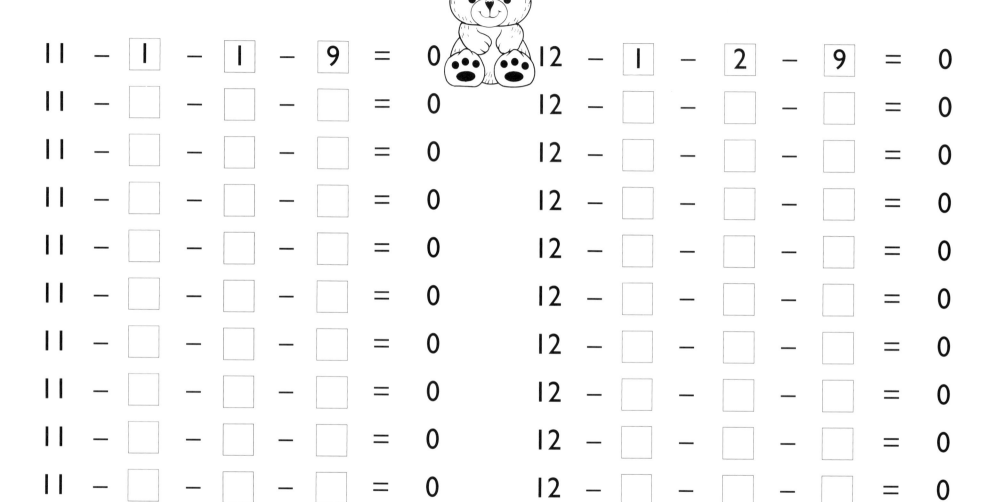

11 − [1] − [1] − [9] = 0   12 − [1] − [2] − [9] = 0

11 − [ ] − [ ] − [ ] = 0   12 − [ ] − [ ] − [ ] = 0

11 − [ ] − [ ] − [ ] = 0   12 − [ ] − [ ] − [ ] = 0

11 − [ ] − [ ] − [ ] = 0   12 − [ ] − [ ] − [ ] = 0

11 − [ ] − [ ] − [ ] = 0   12 − [ ] − [ ] − [ ] = 0

11 − [ ] − [ ] − [ ] = 0   12 − [ ] − [ ] − [ ] = 0

11 − [ ] − [ ] − [ ] = 0   12 − [ ] − [ ] − [ ] = 0

11 − [ ] − [ ] − [ ] = 0   12 − [ ] − [ ] − [ ] = 0

11 − [ ] − [ ] − [ ] = 0   12 − [ ] − [ ] − [ ] = 0

11 − [ ] − [ ] − [ ] = 0   12 − [ ] − [ ] − [ ] = 0

Subtract 3 numbers from 13 and 14. Keep to a pattern. ⇨

The small red bear is learning to play the recorder.
He has to learn 3 notes.

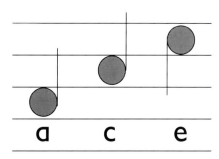

a   c   e

How many different tunes can he play?
Sometimes he plays the same note 3 times.

a c e			

Divide 15 and 16 into 3 groups.

The small yellow bear can pass through a room only once.
Find different ways for him to reach the honey. Start in room 1.
Make a list of the room numbers.

1	2	3	6	5	4	7	8	9

Bedroom ¹	Bathroom ²	Bedroom ³
Living room ⁴	Hall ⁵	Dining Room ⁶
Play Room ⁷	Kitchen ⁸	Pantry ⁹

Honey

Divide 17 and 18 into 3 groups. ⇨

4 bears sit on the mat.

1 square is one quarter of the mat.
2 squares are one half of the mat.
3 squares are three quarters of the mat.

Put 1 bear on one quarter of the mat
        colour the square.

Put 2 bears on one half of the mat
        colour the squares.

Put 3 bears on three quarters of the mat
        colour the squares.

Draw 3 mats. Find different ways to divide them into halves and quarters. ⇨

Put a group of 4 bears in the ring.   Divide the group in half.

How many bears in each half? ☐

Divide the group into quarters.
How many bears in 1 quarter? ☐
in 2 quarters? ☐
in 3 quarters? ☐
in 4 quarters? ☐

Make a group of 6 bears.
Divide the group in half.
How many bears in each half? ☐

Find more groups of bears which divide equally into halves and quarters. ⇨

Line up 8 bears.

Divide the line in half.

Line up half the bears.

How many bears in half of 8?

Line up half the bears again.

How many bears in 1 quarter?

in 2 quarters?

in 3 quarters?

in 4 quarters?

Divide 19 and 20 into three groups. Look for a pattern in the numbers. ⇨

© LDA Compare Bears Maths Book 2

Put 10 green and 10 yellow bears in a bag. Take out 1 bear and record the colour on the graph. Return the bear to the bag. Do this 10 times. Do the same for the other 2 graphs. Are all the graphs the same?

10		
9		
8		
7		
6		
5		
4		
3		
2		
1		
	green	yellow

10		
9		
8		
7		
6		
5		
4		
3		
2		
1		
	green	yellow

10		
9		
8		
7		
6		
5		
4		
3		
2		
1		
	green	yellow

Throw a die 20 times. Record the even and odd numbers. Compare the result with a friend.

even																				
odd																				

1   2   3   4   5   6   7   8   9   10   11   12   13   14   15   16   17   18   19   20

Put 6 blue, 3 green and 3 red bears in a bag. Draw out 1 bear.
Record the colour on the graph. Return the bear to the bag. Repeat 20 times.
Do the same for the second graph. Are both the graphs the same?

red

green

blue

1 2 3 4 5 6 7 8 9 10 11 12 13 14 15 16 17 18 19 20

red

green

blue

1 2 3 4 5 6 7 8 9 10 11 12 13 14 15 16 17 18 19 20

Use 10 red and 10 blue small bears.

20 − 0 = ☐	20 − ☐ = 10	☐ − 10 = 10
20 − 1 = ☐	20 − ☐ = 9	☐ − 10 = 9
20 − 2 = ☐	20 − ☐ = 8	☐ − 10 = 8
20 − 3 = ☐	20 − ☐ = 7	☐ − 10 = 7
20 − 4 = ☐	20 − ☐ = 6	☐ − 10 = 6
20 − 5 = ☐	20 − ☐ = 5	☐ − 10 = 5
20 − 6 = ☐	20 − ☐ = 4	☐ − 10 = 4
20 − 7 = ☐	20 − ☐ = 3	☐ − 10 = 3
20 − 8 = ☐	20 − ☐ = 2	☐ − 10 = 2
20 − 9 = ☐	20 − ☐ = 1	☐ − 10 = 1
20 − 10 = ☐	20 − ☐ = 0	☐ − 10 = 0

Divide 15 and 16 into 3 groups. Look for a pattern. ⇨

Use 10 green and 10 yellow small bears. Keep the 10 green bears together.

10 + 10 = ☐   10 + ☐ = 10   ☐ + 10 = 20

10 + 9 = ☐   10 + ☐ = 11   ☐ + 10 = 19

10 + 8 = ☐   10 + ☐ = 12   ☐ + 10 = 18

10 + 7 = ☐   10 + ☐ = 13   ☐ + 10 = 17

10 + 6 = ☐   10 + ☐ = 14   ☐ + 10 = 16

10 + 5 = ☐   10 + ☐ = 15   ☐ + 10 = 15

10 + 4 = ☐   10 + ☐ = 16   ☐ + 10 = 14

10 + 3 = ☐   10 + ☐ = 17   ☐ + 10 = 13

10 + 2 = ☐   10 + ☐ = 18   ☐ + 10 = 12

10 + 1 = ☐   10 + ☐ = 19   ☐ + 10 = 11

10 + 0 = ☐   10 + ☐ = 20   ☐ + 10 = 10

Divide 17 and 18 bears into 3 groups. Keep to a pattern. ⇨

Use 10 blue and 10 yellow bears. Look for the bonds of ten and the pattern.

0 + 10 + 0 = ☐   20 = 10 + ☐ + 3

1 + 9 + 1 = ☐   20 = 10 + ☐ + 6

2 + 8 + 2 = ☐   20 = 10 + ☐ + 5

3 + 7 + 3 = ☐   20 = 10 + ☐ + 9

4 + 6 + 4 = ☐   20 = 10 + ☐ + 8

5 + 5 + 5 = ☐   20 = 10 + ☐ + 1

6 + 4 + 6 = ☐   20 = 10 + ☐ + 0

7 + 3 + 7 = ☐   20 = 10 + ☐ + 2

8 + 2 + 8 = ☐   20 = 10 + ☐ + 4

9 + 1 + 9 = ☐   20 = 10 + ☐ + 7

10 + 0 + 10 = ☐   20 = 10 + ☐ + 10

Subtract 3 numbers from 15 and 16 to leave 0. Find a pattern for the numbers. ⇨

Use 10 red and 10 green bears. Look for the bonds of ten.

2 + 8 + 10 = ☐

8 + 9 + 2 = ☐

8 + 2 + 8 = ☐

2 + 8 + 7 = ☐

2 + 6 + 8 = ☐

5 + 8 + 2 = ☐

8 + 2 + 4 = ☐

2 + 3 + 8 = ☐

2 + 8 + 2 = ☐

8 + 2 + 1 = ☐

2 + 0 + 8 = ☐

☐ + 0 + 4 = 10

6 + ☐ + 4 = 11

4 + 2 + ☐ = 12

4 + 3 + 6 = ☐

☐ + 4 + 4 = 14

6 + ☐ + 4 = 15

4 + 6 + ☐ = 16

4 + 7 + 6 = ☐

☐ + 8 + 4 = 18

6 + ☐ + 4 = 19

4 + 10 + ☐ = 20

Divide 19 and 20 into 3 groups. Keep the numbers in order. ⇨

Find a small, medium and large bear of each colour. Sort them on to the grid.

	red	blue	green	yellow
lightest				
middle weight				
heaviest				

Draw another grid. Write the colours down the side and the weights across the top.
Re-sort the bears. ⇨

Count in fours and eights. Complete the tables.
Use scales to check the weights.

1   small bear weighs | 4 | g

2   small bears weigh | |

3   _____ | |

4   _____ | |

5   _____ | |

6   _____ | |

7   _____ | |

8   _____ | |

9   _____ | |

10 _____ | |

1   small bear costs | 8 | p

2   small bears cost | |

3   _____ | |

4   _____ | |

5   _____ | |

6   _____ | |

7   _____ | |

8   _____ | |

9   _____ | |

10 _____ | |

Count in eights and tens. Complete the tables.
Use scales to check the weights.

1	medium bear weighs	8 g
2	medium bears weigh	
3	_____	
4	_____	
5	_____	
6	_____	
7	_____	
8	_____	
9	_____	
10	_____	

1	medium bear costs	10 p
2	medium bears cost	
3	_____	
4	_____	
5	_____	
6	_____	
7	_____	
8	_____	
9	_____	
10	_____	

Die template.

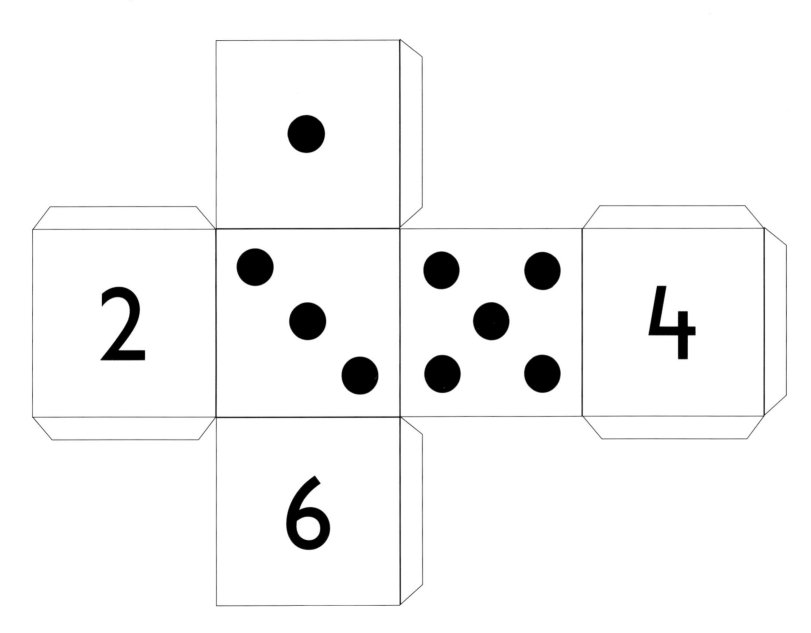

Die template.

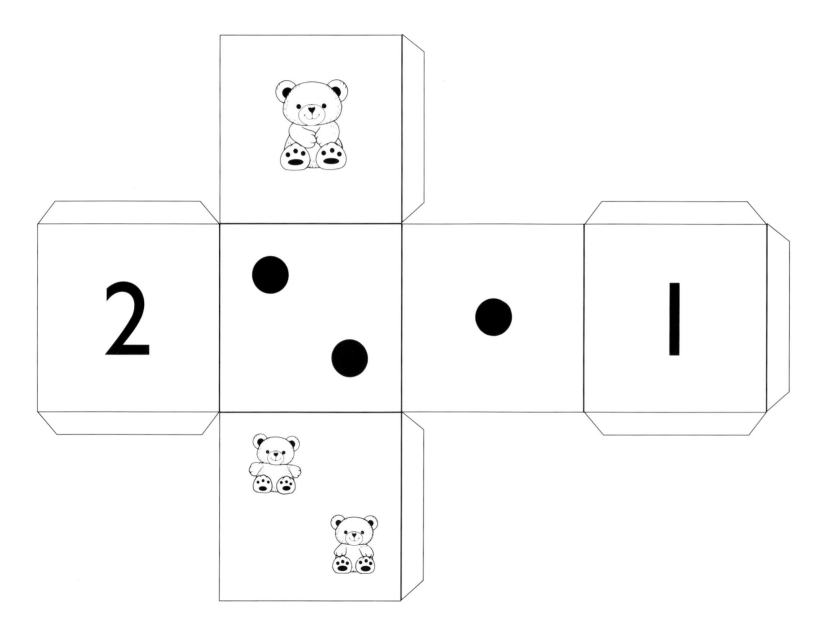

1	2	3	4	5	6	7	8	9	10
11	12	13	14	15	16	17	18	19	20
21	22	23	24	25	26	27	28	29	30
31	32	33	34	35	36	37	38	39	40
41	42	43	44	45	46	47	48	49	50
51	52	53	54	55	56	57	58	59	60
61	62	63	64	65	66	67	68	69	70
71	72	73	74	75	76	77	78	79	80
81	82	83	84	85	86	87	88	89	90
91	92	93	94	95	96	97	98	99	100

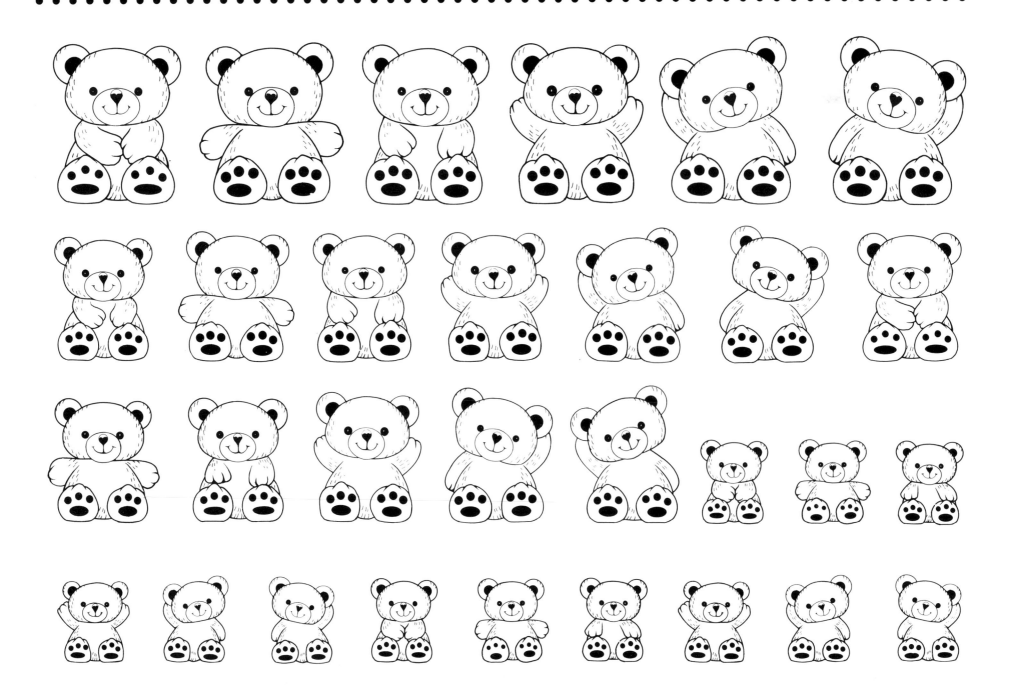